MORE THAN A SONG

*Exploring the Healing Art of
Music Therapy*

Barbara Dunn

MORE THAN A SONG

Exploring the Healing Art of Music Therapy

Copyright © 2012 by Barbara Dunn

ISBN 978-1-937358-09-9

Library of Congress Control Number: [LCCN]
TX 7-560-332

University Book Store Press
4326 University Way NE
Seattle, WA 98105

Cover
Graphic design by Cameron Gray
Original artwork by Barbara Dunn

This book is dedicated to my daughters, Ahna and Emily.
Their singing brings me more joy than they'll ever know.

ACKNOWLEDGEMENTS

This publication would not have been possible without the clients/patients who have trusted me and invited me into their facilities, schools, homes, and hospital rooms to explore how music could help them. I continue to learn from this collaborative exploration of sound and healing. The following people have also been a part of my journey with music in one way or another and I am in debt for their contributions: Jaclyn Weber; Daughters of Harriet (my sisters in song): Jodi Winnwalker, Lisa Jackert, Robin Rio, and Maureen Hearns; Marie Sanger; Barbara Wheeler; Maxine Borowsky Junge; Judy Moore; A.T. Birmingham Young; and Louis Sikes. I am grateful to Emily Dunn-Wilder for her sharp wit and insightful eye in reviewing this publication. Additionally, my work over the years would never have been possible without the loving support of my family: David Wilder, Ahna Dunn-Wilder, and Emily Dunn-Wilder. I feel blessed to have their encouragement and presence in my life.

TABLE OF CONTENTS

TABLE OF SONGS AND POEMS

**To Sing
Is to Give the Spoken Word a Way to Dance!**

INTRODUCTION

Who has not been affected by music in some way? Whether using it to provide comfort, joy or ease from stress, music has a definite place in most people's lives. For some, the quiet sound of a harp might offer the greatest comfort. For others, singing at the top of his or her lungs might be the only way to address a strong emotion. Whatever the situation, music can ease into the space between words and feelings to enliven, soothe and heal. The art of using music as therapy is about being open to whatever direction the music needs to go.

For more than twenty-five years I have made my living as a music therapist. I have worked in state-run hospitals for the mentally ill, group homes for people with developmental disabilities, nursing facilities for older adults or people with AIDS, medical hospitals, home health and hospice agencies, and schools – from preschools to universities. I have worked with the medically fragile and the emotionally distraught, from younger to older. The common denominator of using music in all of these settings is the humanness of each person (regardless of the challenges they face) and the way that music can reach her or him in a unique way. Each one of us hears music that is mixed with emotions felt in the moment and associations related to a host of

1

other factors, such as the instrumentation, words of a song… This explains how two people can listen to the same piece of music and one is moved to tears and the other is bored to tears. Music therapy can address those tears with understanding and compassion.

For some people verbal communication does not come easily but they can communicate with music. Perhaps a stroke has limited their ability to speak but they can still sing. Sometimes playing an instrument is just the motivation needed to work on regaining physical use of a hand after an accident. Physical or emotional pain can be eased in the melodic line of a song. Intense feelings can begin to be expressed by playing or listening to a poignant song. Aldous Huxley (1931) noted, "After silence that which comes nearest to expressing the inexpressible is music" (p. 17). Whatever the challenge, music can be a tool to help, heal or soothe, or to simply accompany one's path through life.

Music can touch the heart and be felt in the body even when a person claims they are not "musical." There are no prerequisites to feeling or being moved by music. I have found that a person who is near death and seemingly unresponsive can still feel the rhythm of a song. They might acknowledge the rhythm with a slight nod of the head or a tapping of the toe or even steady, rhythmic breathing. I know they are moving in response to my music because they physically react when I make a rhythmic mistake. The reaction might be slight but it is exactly at the time of my rhythmic mistake. When music is performed with sensitivity and accuracy it can provide a sense of predictability and comfort.

Music is like a current running through my life. It is wonderful to help others find a similar "current," whether through professional or personal settings. My children have grown up with music and I hear them singing spontaneously throughout their day. It reminds me of my mother singing throughout the house as I grew up. Whatever the setting, it is the joy of music that connects us to each other and, potentially, to the very essence of our being.

People often ask me about my work. If I begin with the training, research or history of music therapy, I will sometimes note a glossed-over look in their face, a blank stare. When I describe a patient or client and something we did together with music, they breathe a noticeable sigh, heads nod, they smile, they lean forward. The intention of this book is to provide that leaned-forward glimpse into this beautiful world where music can create change and promote healing. It begins with stories taken from my work with people facing a wide variety of challenges. Each of these sections is followed by lyrics to a related song. Most of the songs are originals inspired by my work. I find that writing songs provides a vehicle for distilling information to reveal the essence of a topic. The second part of the book fills in some basic information about the field of music therapy, selected research in music and music therapy, and some of the tools I have found to be invaluable in my work. Please feel free to skip around and read the book in whatever order makes sense to you.

CLINICAL VIGNETTES

All of these stories are taken from my clinical experiences. Some are taken from a single session while others span experiences that occurred over several years. For the most part, I have changed names of people and altered descriptions to protect confidentiality. Permission has been granted in the few instances where real names are used. Use of the terms "patient" or "client" is generally reflective of the work setting; medical facilities frequently use the term "patient" while nonmedical facilities tend to use the term "client." It has been an honor to work with so many people at such challenging times in their lives.

AIDS

Early into a new job at a nursing facility specializing in care for people with AIDS, I was asked to visit **Philip**. The month was December, Christmas was near and Philip was actively dying from AIDS. When I entered the room he was lying in bed, his partner was with him and they asked if I knew the song *Christmas in the Trenches* by John McCutcheon (1984). This was a very special song to them. The song describes a Christmas Eve in France during World War I where a temporary truce took place: "neither gun, nor bayonet, we met there hand to hand." The soldiers shared "chocolates, cigarettes and photographs from home." Together they sang *Silent Night/Stihle Nacht* and "in two tongues, one song filled up that sky." When morning came, each soldier was faced with the question of who might be on the other side of his rifle. The walls between them had crumbled and the value of human life rested heavy in the air. It is a very poignant song that was even more so given Philip's situation.

I sang what I could remember of the song and went home to learn the song in its entirety. I returned a couple of days later with the song but I was a few minutes too late. Philip had just died. His body was still in the room as were his partner and his mother. We formed a circle around him and I sang the song. In those moments, the spirit of the Christmas season had been forever altered, just as it had been for those soldiers in World War I. The lights were dim and there was a hushed sense about the room. I felt that Philip was still with us, lingering and blessing us with his spirit.

Just down the hall from Philip's room was **Joan**, who asked me to help her get back to playing her guitar. Like many persons with AIDS, Joan had good days and bad days. This particular day was a good one. She was trying to work out the chords to a Pete Seeger song called *Old Devil Time*. We worked out the chords and then sang the song together:

"Old devil time, I'm gonna fool you now, old devil time you'd like to bring me down, when I'm feelin' low, my lovers gather 'round and help me rise to fight you one more time. Old devil fear, you with your icy hand, old devil fear, you'd like to freeze me cold, but when I'm afraid, my lovers gather 'round and help me rise to fight you one more time."
(Seeger, 1969)

Joan had a large network of support. She had been active in the gay community and worked extensively with AIDS advocacy groups. She was comfortable talking about AIDS and her situation but singing the song gave her a chance to express it in a different way. It allowed for physical release with the feel of the

8

strings under her fingers, the rhythm of her strum, and the melody riding on the breath and tone of her voice. The words also went directly to a place where she felt the intensity of AIDS: "Old devil fear, you with your icy hand; old devil fear, you'd like to freeze me cold. When I'm afraid, my lovers gather 'round..."

Another man in the facility, **Matthew**, was absolutely one of the nicest people I had ever met. He always greeted me with a warm smile and kind words. I remember Matthew and the gentle way he always inquired about the welfare of others, even when he himself was experiencing immense physical and emotional challenges. Matthew always had room in his heart for others. At this particular facility, I supervised a team of volunteers who also played music for people. Every one of these musicians had a special relationship with Matthew. As his disease progressed he developed AIDS-related dementia, which affected his ability to process normal thought patterns. Matthew's favorite song was *Moonshadow* by Cat Stevens (1971). I sang this song to him every week when I visited him. Every week he would smile and sing along until one day he very gently and sweetly said, "Do you know any other songs?"

AIDS has many edges to its sword. The edges can appear when communication with a loved one becomes difficult, when every physical movement causes pain, when the drugs necessary to fight the disease cause intense nausea and/or vomiting. I found that music could go to all of those places affected by this sword. Improvisation on the piano allowed feelings to be expressed and communicated without having to find the exact words. Focus on live or recorded music allowed the mind to focus on something other than the pain. Music helped to relax those stomach muscle spasms caused by the nausea or vomiting. Engaging in music-making allowed time to think about something other than AIDS. More than once I heard a patient comment, "Wow, I didn't think about AIDS for this entire hour." The music provided a break from a disease they lived with every moment of their day.

When I first began my work with people who had AIDS, I was struck by the sheer number of persons struggling with the disease and the young age of many of the victims. It was 1995 and our facility was witnessing nearly one dozen deaths per month from AIDS. At this time in my career, I had more than ten years under my belt of playing music in nursing homes, mostly with older adults. Now the patients I worked with were my contemporaries; the songs I sang were songs of my youth. I have been forever changed by this work.

Writing this song provided me with an opportunity to process my feelings and experiences with people who have AIDS. The lyrical inspiration came from the notion in Jewish tradition that people are kept alive by our remembering of them.

I WILL REMEMBER YOU
Barbara Dunn

There's a knot in my stomach and it's growing,
There's a pain in my heart and a knowing
A knowing of injustice, a disease we can't explain
One that causes so much pain.
Someone lost his life today
All his dreams have slipped away,
Can we do no more than pray?

There're names to these faces and I hear them.
There're so many faces, I see them.
Sharing their dreams and what they've learned about life,
Wisdom that comes from their strife.
I will remember you
And carry your dreams with me
Help the world to see.

I see the suffering and hear the families cry.
It's a holocaust occurring before my eyes.
I'm trying to make some sense of it and salvage the dreams.
Keep the threads while losing the seams.
I will remember you.
I will remember you.
I will remember you.

11

ALZHEIMER'S DISEASE

"Pardon me, boys, is that the Chattanooga Choo Choo…" As I sang this popular song (Gordon & Warren, 1941) **Joe** opened his eyes. He was alert and smiling. Before I came into the room, he was sitting in his chair sound asleep. He slept much of the day lately. Joe was experiencing the end stages of Alzheimer's disease. He was slipping from us day by day, yet music was still the one thing that could bring him back to the present. When I sang to him, his eyes opened and he listened. He played his mandolin with me. He also played the piano and drums. On occasion, I could get him to dance with me. Joe played music most of his life; it brought him joy and a way to express himself. It was no different now. While we played music together, I could sometimes look into his eyes and see the person who was there before the disease began to take him away. The spark had returned, if only for a moment.

"F-F-F-Flora, beautiful Flora, you're the only g-g-g-girl that I adore..." With the beginning of this song **Flora's** face would light up. She did not know *my* name from week to week but she always knew *her* name. It represented the essence of spirit that would always be Flora - even while Alzheimer's disease slowly took away the other recognizable traces of her personality. Flora was a member of a weekly music therapy group where we sang familiar songs, danced to recorded music, learned new songs and even wrote some of our own. Flora and her friends were able to learn the routines of the weekly group. The old familiar songs were a way for them to remember who they were; the new songs and experiences gave them a way to continue to grow and learn.

I also worked with Joe in this group, in addition to our individual sessions. Being in the group gave him a social context in which to play his music. This is particularly poignant when he and others in the group had such difficulty remaining connected with others. It is a great joy to help someone awaken to music, to see the light go on and know, in that moment, you have connected with another human being...connected through music!

I learned this song many years ago but have been unable to find out who wrote the lyrics and music. The lyrics poignantly portray the experience of losing a loved one to Alzheimer's disease.

IT'S A LONG GOODBYE
Author Unknown

She's leaving me, little by little, I wish she wouldn't go.
I will be there as long as she needs me, how do I let her know?

I'd like to hold on to the memories, I'd also like to share.
But she's further away, getting further away.
And yet, she's always there.

It's a long good-bye, and yet I believe that she can sense us.
So much time between now and then, why is time against us?

These are the times she almost seems like herself.
Sometimes it's just a phase. Part of the person I once knew,
Sometimes just a trace.

It's a long good-bye and still I don't know just what to say.
There's so much time between now and then,
before she goes away.

It's a long good-bye.
Tell me how do all the others do it?
There's so much time between now and then.
How do we get through it? It's a long good-bye.
It's a long good-bye.

15

ALS -AMYOTROPHIC LATERAL SCLEROSIS
Lou Gehrig's Disease

Les sat back and closed his eyes as I sang one of his favorite songs. He was in the final stages of his struggles with Amyotrophic Lateral Sclerosis (ALS). We had just met and were trying to sort out how music could help him at this time in his life. He had been a professional musician for most of his life and music was still very dear to him. When we began talking about composing music, his face lit up. He told me about some music he had written long ago. He had never gotten around to writing the music down or recording it. We decided that putting his music into a manuscript format would be a project we would work on together.

Over the next several weeks we put together two songs. Les sat by my side as I tried to correctly play his melodies on the piano. This was no easy task for either of us. He was getting weaker by the day and his strength could not endure long sessions. Nevertheless, it seemed to be important to him and he persevered through the pain and effort. For my part, I was challenged both musically and therapeutically. Les would sing the song as I wrote down the melody and rhythm. His illness caused his voice to crack and made it difficult for him to hold an exact pitch. This, in turn, made it difficult for me to transcribe the song accurately and Les was always quick to let me know if I got it right or wrong. Sometimes he would have the strength to play the notes himself on the piano. His muscle control was not terribly steady so this, too, was a challenge. Therapeutically, I had to constantly weigh each moment to be sure my encouragement wasn't pushing him past what he could physically endure. For the most part, Les determined how far we would go in each given session. When the communication was successful and I correctly played his songs for him, an incredible look of satisfaction came over his face and he broke out with a beautiful smile.

One of the songs we worked on was about his mother. He told me that she died in his arms thirty years ago. He wrote this song for her. The sacredness of the task was not lost on either of us. We were singing a song for his mother and reflecting upon her death as Les's own death loomed in the near future.

We were able to complete our work together on his two original compositions before he was no longer able to sit up in his wheelchair. The last time I saw Les he was in his bed and, at his request, I sang some of his favorite songs. I also sang his songs. Upon hearing his own music, he brightened and a very satisfied smile rested on his face. As he lay back in his bed, he told me he could listen to those songs all day.

The next time I went to Les's home, his wife told me he was reserving all of his remaining energy for communication with his family. He was very weak and had stopped eating. While I did not have a chance to personally say goodbye to Les, I was able to leave his family with a copy of the written manuscript of his music. I also gave them a recording I had made of the songs. This recording was played for him before he passed away and will remain as a gift from Les to his family.

This song is printed here with permission from Les's family.

SPANISH LULLABY
Les Hewitt

Close your eyes, go to sleep, hear the sweet guitars.
Dream you on a bed of clouds; sprinkle down with stars.

Mother's near, Daddy, too; listen for a sigh.
You will wake with a smile, Spanish Lullaby.

Sleep while angels dance above.
Dream while señoritas love.
Angels watching over you
Will let the Sandman lead you
While you sleep.

Soon the dawn will break through
Your sunshine fill the sky.
You will wake with your smile
Spanish Lullaby.

ANXIETY

Rebecca had anxiety and generalized fears that limited her ability to cope in her daily life. Her fears kept her from going into stores and facing situations where she had to respond to requests made of her. One challenge that often came up for her was counting out money to pay the cashier at a store. Having to count out payment or collect change after a purchase was seriously distressing to her. This was most exasperating when there was a line of people behind her. We figured out some practical ways to deal with the situation, from using a credit card where she only needed to sign the receipt to using only dollar bills, collecting her change and dropping it into her purse. That still did not address the anxiety that built up before even entering the store. For this, Rebecca and I identified music that relaxed her. This was not difficult as she was a classically trained cellist and had an extensive collection of recorded music at her home. We paired specific recordings with relaxation techniques that included deep, slow breathing and progressive muscle relaxation. Eventually, she was able to trigger a relaxation response in her body just by turning on the music. We also worked with a portable CD player and headphones. She was able to softly play the music while she engaged in other activities, such as entering a store and shopping.

The music helped her to feel calm and, thus, better attend to her task at hand. Later she was able to simply listen to the music in the car, gain her composure and enter the store in a more relaxed manner.

Dental fear is common for many people, including me. Imagine your dentist telling you, "There is a lot of decay under the old filling and it will take us awhile to clean it out. There's a chance we'll need to perform a root canal. It could take several hours." How many cringe at the thought of even *one* hour in the dentist's chair? Recorded music is the only way I can make it through dental procedures; in fact, I never go to the dentist without my iPod or CD player and headphones. The key is to have music that I find inspiring and engaging. If the music is too calm and relaxing, it will be incongruent with the anxiety-provoking experience. In other words, the music has to somewhat match my mood at the dentist's office – very different from the music I might play for a quiet candlelit dinner with my family. Once I settle into the dentist's chair and get the "go ahead" from my dentist, I put the headphones on and press "play." The music starts with the first needle poke of anesthesia. I find that having my finger on the volume button helps because it gives me a sense of control; I can match the volume of music to the sound of the drill. (Caution: do not have the volume so loud that it causes damage to your eardrums.) Sometimes the *sounds* in the dentist office stimulate the most fears. The last time I was in the dentist's chair for a procedure, I selected Jennifer Warnes's 1986 recording, *Famous Blue Raincoat, Songs of Leonard Cohen*. I found myself pushing the repeat button on the song *Joan of Arc*. Somehow the words gave me a sense of camaraderie and comfort: "Now the flames they followed Joan of Arc as she came riding through the dark; no moon to keep her armor bright, no man to get her through this dark and smoky night" (Cohen, 1971).

Another way I use music to assist with medical procedures is by singing through them. I am embarrassed to admit that I am a big baby when it comes to even the simplest shot or blood draw. Singing has always given me a way to relax and has become a useful tool for even the least bit of pain. When I get a blood draw or a shot, I look the other way and sing my heart out. So far I have not received complaints about my singing from medical personnel. If only I could sing during dental procedures!

Meditation can be a very useful tool for people with anxiety. A meditative Buddhist practice called Metta (or loving-kindness) offers a way to bring peace into our lives. It involves focused attention first inward and then outward to people in our lives and in the world at large. The following is a simple chant I wrote that uses concepts and words of this loving-kindness meditation.

METTA CHANT
Barbara Dunn

May I be safe
        inside and outside.
And hold myself in kindness,
        loving me now.
May I be well
        of mind and body.
May I have peace
        with ease in my day.

May you be safe
        inside and outside.
And hold yourself in kindness,
        loving you now.
May you be well
        of mind and body.
May you have peace
        with ease in your day.

AUTISM

From across the room, I sang out part of an Italian aria. When I got to the high G in the song, **Brian** started singing with me... on the same note! Brian was seven years old and had autism. It was difficult to find a "way in" to communicate with him; this high G was my way in.

Brian did not easily respond to people in his environment. He sometimes sang parts of Christmas songs but not usually with others. More often than not, he would sing to himself and remain in his own world. From this high G that we sang together we moved on to more singing and playing music together. His family joined us in music making for about ten minutes at the end of every session. Typically, Brian communicated with his family via a combination of gestures and minimal vocal sounds. Using music, Brian now had an additional tool or language that he could use to express his feelings and thoughts, a tool that could be used by Brian and his family. Playing music also offered a way for all to simply be together and have fun.

We continued to use music during our sessions to develop communication strategies. His family joined us and, in the music therapy clinical setting, we had some success. Overall, however, we were not so successful. The intervention is only as powerful as its ability to be replicated in situations occurring in ordinary life outside of the therapy setting. For Brian to use music at home to express himself and communicate, his family needed to commit to music making and to making music accessible for Brian. One suggestion was to have musical instruments in central gathering places. Even though I had several sessions at the home, I was not able to convince the family to change their environment or their relationship to music. They accepted that Brian was drawn to music and that he could sing even though he did not talk. Unfortunately, they did not increase or adjust their use of music in the home. Thus, the music therapy sessions were not nearly as effective as they could have been. To have a true impact, an attitude shift sometimes needs to occur. In my heart of hearts, however, I can still hear that high G and I have hopes that it will re-emerge in another aria somewhere in Brian's lifetime.

Erin was in her 40s and also had autism. With autism, intellectual ability varies from individual to individual, as in the non-autistic population. Erin was bright and had much to communicate even though she was unable to speak. She wrote poetry that gave voice to the thoughts that she was unable to express verbally. Sometimes I would sing those poems to her and she accompanied with instrumental playing and vocalizing on specific vowels. Sometimes she would just stop and listen to her words as I sang them. She listened with careful attention as if weighing each of the words, each of her thoughts. On a couple of occasions, we went into a recording studio and recorded these songs. Music and poetry were very important to Erin. They offered her a unique connection to the world she was otherwise unable to access.

Erin has graciously given me permission to include her poem in this book.

ROSES
Erin Eyer

Roses flowering in the garden lose their beauty when wistful people snip them, averaging the pollen of love. Under the operation of the therapy under the roof of innovation of golden sun fragrance ferments the passageways of our lives acting as our guides making sure our putrid existence has glory at heaven's gate.

28

CANCER

At the time I met **Carol**, she had a large cancerous tumor in her stomach. She was interested in music therapy and eager to add whatever she could to her treatment plan. She was determined to do whatever it took to beat her disease. We decided to work with music and imagery. We identified recorded music that she found relaxing. We used the music with techniques that included deep, slow breathing, progressive muscle relaxation and creative visualization. We worked with the movement of the music and a vision of light moving around the tumor. She imagined the light and the music moving through and breaking up the tumor, and ultimately, moving the tumor out of the body. Carol and I met three to four times to fine tune her work with the music and visualization. She continued with her course of chemotherapy and radiation and used the music visualization until she was, eventually, cancer-free. Did the music help to get rid of her tumor? There is no way to know for sure. At the very least, it helped her to feel calm and gave her an active role in her treatment.

Bill had lost the ability to speak due to a large tumor in his throat. The tumor caused him pain and great frustration over his inability to communicate. He used a pen, pad of paper, and facial expressions to convey his thoughts and feelings. Music had always been a very important part of his life; listening to music still gave him a great deal of pleasure and comfort. One day I was sitting with him and he wrote down a song for me to sing. It was *This Little Light of Mine*. When I finished singing, he wrote that it was a favorite Sunday school song from his youth. He continued requesting songs from his childhood. With each song he would lie back in his bed, sigh and close his eyes. With some of the songs, he wrote down when he first sang them or a special meaning attached to the song. Mostly, however, he just listened and let his body fall into the memories. When I was finished, it was as if we had traveled throughout the entirety of his life. He appeared satiated and at peace.

Nicole was a beautiful person with an incredibly musical spirit. She had been a vibrant participant in our weekly music therapy group. When her health began to decline, I visited her in her room. Her speech was barely audible and difficult to understand. Her body appeared weak and frail. Looking at her, I tried to imagine what was going on in her mind and in her heart. I began singing *Amazing Grace*, a song we had sung together in the past. She shook her head indicating that this was not the correct song for this particular moment. With a significant effort, I was able to ascertain what she was trying to tell me. Nicole whispered softly, "I'm not there yet!" I asked her what song I could sing that would describe where she was in that moment. She replied, *The Glory of Love*. I smiled and sang the words written by Billy Hill (1936), "You gotta give a little, take a little, and let your poor heart break a little, that's the glory of, that's the story of love." As I sang, Nicole joined me in singing with her soft voice and beautiful, unfaltering spirit.

Few people have not been touched in some way by cancer. One day I was describing my work to my daughter's second grade class. When I mentioned that some people I work with have cancer, four to five children's hands immediately went up. They each wanted to tell me a story about someone they knew who had cancer. I was impressed with the simple and honest thoughts they expressed. One child said, "People die when they have cancer," another said, "My aunt has cancer." I matter-of-factly explained that people *do not* always die when they have cancer but *sometimes they do*. I told the children that cancer is part of our world and that it is okay to talk about it.

In many ways, cancer remains a mystery. Even with knowledge of risk factors and hereditary predisposition, it can seem to strike out of the blue. The natural shock and fear that can come from a diagnosis of cancer can be devastating and overwhelming. Music can address this myriad of emotions in the

31

moment of a song. The music might be a ballad that expresses love or loss or fear. It might be an aria that is sung so beautifully that emotions can ride with the melody through the wide range of highs and lows. Music can offer comfort and companionship in a tender and challenging situation.

This song is here in dedication to my co-workers in the oncology clinic at Whidbey General Hospital where I have witnessed exceptional quality of care combined with the utmost grace and compassion.

HOLD MY HAND
Barbara Dunn

Hold my hand.

'Twas grace that brought me to this place and

Held my hand

Now I'll walk you through this land.

CHILDBIRTH

I have been honored to be part of birth teams for several women. Most of the births occurred in the women's private homes with the assistance of a midwife who was also a naturopathic doctor. The births occurred without the use of any pharmacological pain medication. Music offered a tool to address pain and to enhance the quality of the birthing experience.

One woman I worked with was having a very long labor that lasted more than 30 hours. The contractions were weak and, thus, she was not in excruciating pain. She was very interested in using music to help her through this process. We decided to try vocalizing on vowel sounds during her contractions. Thus, the room would periodically erupt into improvised and harmonic tones. Instead of yelling during contraction, as is common during the birth process, she allowed the melodic line of her singing to carry her through the waves of pain. She said the vocalizing helped to release tension caused by her pain and discomfort. The midwife involved commented that she had a hard time gauging the severity of the contractions, as she had never had anyone "sing" through them before. It is interesting to note that when the intensity of pain increased, as the actual birth drew near, she continued to use her voice in this way. Before the birth, we created a compilation of recorded music that she planned to use during labor. As it turned out, she preferred to use her voice rather than the recorded music. She did play the tape shortly after the birth. It was the perfect music to welcome her beautiful child into the world.

Another birth I participated in was very different from the one described above. It was a shorter labor with intense contractions coming at regular intervals. As with the other woman, we had worked with recorded music to be able to use it for the birth process. A couple of months before the actual birth, we selected three CDs that she found to be relaxing. The music she selected had steady movement, but was not too fast. It consisted of some of her favorite musical instruments: guitar, piano, flute, and oboe. We worked together using relaxation techniques combined with the music. She practiced relaxing to these particular recordings so that when she heard them during the birth, her body would know how to relax to the music. As previously stated, her contractions were intense and during them she went straight to yelling, or as described by her three-year-old daughter: "My mommy roared like a lion!" In between the contractions, she focused on the music. Those few minutes of relaxation with music gave her enough rest and strength to handle the contractions and to see her through to the birth of her very sweet newborn baby.

I wrote this lullaby for my daughters when they were young.

SING A LULLABY
Barbara Dunn

I will sing a lullaby to guide you through the night.
I'm here if you should cry, I'll love you and hold you tight.
I will sing a lullaby to guide you through the night.

I know it's dark in your room, there's a fear inside of you,
But hang on, dear, for I will not leave you.
The shadows on the wall are only there for show,
When light comes in, they'll be gone you know.

Now I see you as you sleep, your face is so at peace.
Not a care in the air or calling out needs.
And as you lie so calm, I think of your world ahead.
You'll go on and explore, leaving this warm, safe bed.

I will sing a lullaby to guide you through the night.
I'm here if you should cry, I'll love you and hold you tight.
I will sing a lullaby to guide you through the night.

DEVELOPMENTAL DISABILITIES

Dorothy suffered trauma at birth that limited oxygen to her brain and left her with a developmental disability. She grew up in a state-run institution for people with developmental disabilities. In this institutional setting, Dorothy found that music helped give her joy and an opportunity to express herself. She told me she learned to play the accordion by watching Myron Floren on The Lawrence Welk Show during the 1950s. Dorothy developed an exceptional aptitude for music with a very good sense of both pitch and rhythm. When I played four notes simultaneously, she was able to tell me the name of all the notes. I could sing a new song to her and she immediately sang it back to me with complete accuracy. Sometimes the tempo of her songs dragged but if I played along with her at an upbeat tempo, she easily kept time with me. I once took her to John's Music Center in Seattle. This is a fabulous music store with many instruments from all around the world. Being in that store is like being a small child in a candy shop – all the instruments were calling out to be played. Before I knew it, Dorothy was on the drums jamming with a group of guys who also happened to be there playing on the drums. They jammed together for about 20 minutes. One of the drummers was so taken by her enthusiasm and skill that he bought her a drum after he learned that she did not have one of her own.

At the time I met Dorothy, she was in her late fifties and lived in a group home with other adults who also had developmental disabilities. Throughout her life she had learned many "old time" favorite songs on her accordion and she loved to perform them. It seemed fitting for her musical gifts to be shared with others. We developed a plan wherein she led sing-alongs with her accordion for older adults in nearby nursing homes. Many of the older adults loved to hear the accordion and to sing familiar songs. We put together a songbook with lyrics to these songs for the nursing homes. Dorothy received a small payment from the nursing home for leading the sing-along. This was a higher hourly wage than she had ever received and exponentially larger than her bi-weekly income from her job at a sheltered workshop. For the first time in her life, Dorothy was being paid for her music! The program was a good deal for the nursing home as well: it was inexpensive and it gave the residents a chance to sing and reminisce with familiar songs. The benefits for Dorothy were many; she was proud of her work, she was interacting with others and she had extra cash in her pocket. Another plus was that this program found a way for a person with a developmental disability to give back to the community. People need to feel useful; people with developmental disabilities are no exception. Dorothy was acknowledged for her strengths and unique talents rather than noted for her disability.

People with developmental disabilities can have difficulties expressing themselves and communicating with others. Music can address these challenges and offer a way to express and communicate, thus reaching beyond physical, emotional and social barriers. I have worked with individuals whose disabilities were so severe they were unable to speak and needed assistance for all of their activities of daily living (eating, walking, toileting). I remember working with one man who was unable to communicate with words and showed very limited involvement with his environment. It was the winter holiday season with holly, ivy, lights, and songs of Christmas everywhere. As I sang familiar carols to this man something seemed to click: his eyes lit up and, for a few moments, I saw a definite spark. During those moments, we were able to communicate an understanding that went beyond words.

Kari Cunningham-Rosvik, MA, MN, ARNP, works with people with developmental disabilities in her private practice. She has written about a mother's journey of healing when her daughter was born with a disability.

THE SLEEP OF ANGELS
Kari Cunningham-Rosvik

My daughter you sleep with the sleep of an innocent.
Your breathing is deep and even, your arms wide open to receive
the dreams of angels.
I want to freeze us in this moment and hold on to it forever.

In the early years, sorrow was an unwelcome companion.
It clouded my ability to see who you really were
and to recognize your perfection from the moment you were born.

Sadness still visits my heart sometimes
but I have learned to embrace our life together and
to realize there is so much more.

There is joy for your accomplishments, laughter for
your impish humor and tricks.
There is pride for your beauty and respect for how you touch and
change others.
There is compassion for my sorrow and strength for the journey
that lay ahead.

It is late my child.
Continue to sleep with the sleep of an innocent.
Let your arms rest open to receive the love that is yours.
Now is the time to sleep and receive the dreams of angels.

HOSPICE CARE

In all my years of work as a music therapist, the most profound experiences have come from the hospice setting. It only takes a moment in the presence of someone who is dying to know what is truly important in life. I have been blessed to be part of this journey with my patients.

Frank asked me to come to his home for a music therapy session with his family. He was in the last weeks of his life and his entire family had joined him at their seaside home. When I arrived, the family was gathered in the living room with several generations represented. I had not met anyone in this family before I entered their home, but there I was, guitar in hand – ready and willing to embrace the moments ahead. We sang songs of faith, life, trials and triumphs; there were tears and laughter mixed throughout the session. At one point Frank sang *Ol' Man River,* from Jerome Kern and Oscar Hammerstein's 1927 musical *Show Boat*. Many eyes in the room filled with tears as he sang "Ah gets weary and sick of trying, I'm tired of living and scared of dying." It was a very tender moment. It was also nearing the time to end our session; we needed a song that would honor this tenderness, allow for closure, and bring some peace to this family. As I searched my brain for the perfect song, a five-year-old grandchild began singing "Make new friends but keep the old, one is silver and the other gold." We all held hands in a circle and sang the last verse, led by this five-year-old child, "I have a hand, you have another, put them together and we have each other."

Bringing peace to the moment requires a keen awareness of how the music is being received and the evoked response. This was made very clear to me when I was asked to use music to help **James** with his symptoms. He was unable to communicate verbally, but facial grimaces, moans, and writhing of his body indicated a great deal of pain and agitation. I stood at his bedside with my guitar and began to play something quiet and, I thought, soothing. James became more agitated. I then played something fast with a driving tempo and greater volume. In what seemed like an instant, the moaning stopped, his body relaxed and his face expression was peaceful. I had finally spoken to him in a language he could understand. I later learned that James had grown up in a part of Africa where rhythmic music was an important part of his daily living. Rhythmic music now offered a place of comfort for James.

Sarah had been estranged from her brother for many years. Now that she was dying, she wanted to connect with her brother but was not sure how. I encouraged her to write some thoughts down about her feelings in poetry or in the form of a letter. Later that day, Sarah composed a letter for her brother. When I returned the following week, I read the letter and we discussed a couple of options. She could send the letter as is or we could put the letter to music. Sarah requested that I put the words to music for her. I ended up singing the letter in an improvisatory style with guitar accompaniment. I enlisted the help of Stanley Greenthal (a musician I worked with in this hospice setting) and we recorded it at his home-based recording studio. Stanley helped give it a full sound with a beautiful guitar interlude. We then recorded the music and I gave Sarah a copy. She was delighted with the recording and played it for nearly everyone who visited her. The entire process was powerful in that it provided her an opportunity to experience her feelings from a distance with another voice singing her thoughts and feelings. It gave her a vehicle for exploring her thoughts and feelings and, ultimately, communicating them to her estranged brother. He did end up visiting her and they were able to experience some healing and closure before she passed away.

In and out of consciousness, **Michael** was actively dying. I entered his room, guitar in hand. I could hear the soft sound of his breathing. There was a sense of hush and reverence in the room where a couple of loved ones gathered to be with him. I began playing something quiet and soothing on my guitar. After a few minutes, he gently opened his eyes and looked straight at me. Then he asked, in a very clear voice, "Do you know any Elvis?" Fortunately, I was able to pull a couple of Elvis tunes from my repertoire.

I have been honored to provide music at the bedside as someone is actively dying. This is the time when the body begins to shut down, breathing and sleeping patterns may change. Even into the first couple notes of the music, I can sometimes sense the body letting go and giving in to the sounds it hears. The music fills the air to soothe fear and discomfort, not only for the patient but also for loved ones gathered. Music can move in with ease and grace, matching the pace of breath with the rhythm of the music, the tone of the room with the softness of the voice. It is with a feeling of reverence and awe that I enter into the room. There is no discussion of "illness" or "disease." All that matters is the moment and in this moment there is a sense of the sacred and there is music.

I wrote the following song as collected thoughts of persons leaving this world and yet wanting so much to remain with loved ones, in whatever way possible.

I WILL NOT DIE
Barbara Dunn

I will not die, not while you live,
My life and dreams will go on with you.

Though you see me lying here with dis-ease,
I cannot stand or hold onto your hand.
But in my heart, I still dance with ease,
So, won't you continue on, please?

Yes, it's unfair that I should be here.
I cannot convey the depth of my fear.
Will I go in my sleep; will the pain be felt deep?
With my final cry, will you be by my side?

I've had my share of travels and affairs,
Still there is more I'd love to explore.
But I have no regrets; it's all been worthwhile,
The good and the bad, the joyful and sad.

My body is gone, there's no being to hold.
But my love will remain and never grow old.
I'm there with you now; I'm holding you still.
Please carry my love; I'll trust that you will.

I will not die, not while you live,
My life and dreams will go on with you.

LUNG DISEASE

Susan struggled to take another breath. Every inhalation created a sense of fear that the air taken in would not be enough. She often would tense her body and gasp for air. Sometimes tears fell with the sheer struggle. In a chair beside her bed, I began playing a soft melody on my guitar. With the opening notes of the music the tension in her muscles relaxed, her face softened and she appeared more at ease. The music was able to move softly into her pain and give her body a chance to be calm. With a gentle suggestion, she was then able to visualize a place of beauty where she was comfortable and breathing required less effort. We worked with this process to help her find a way to live with her progressively limited lung capacity.

People with lung disease can find themselves dealing with a variety of challenging symptoms, from shortness of breath to anxiety related to that shortness of breath. The same techniques used in singing can be helpful for someone with these symptoms. **Lucy** struggled with Cardio Obstructive Pulmonary Disease (COPD), a common disease affecting the lungs. She was born and raised in Ireland and sang her entire life. It was extremely frustrating to her that she could no longer sing as she used to. Her vocal tone was weak and she was unable to sustain notes for very long. She was even having difficulty carrying on a conversation (which had also been a big part of her life). Anything we could do to enhance Lucy's breath support would be helpful. The breath support used for proper singing technique is the same support that could also help her with her speaking voice. It includes using the abdominal muscles and expanding them out to make as much room as possible for the lungs to expand. This type of breathing is in contrast to shallow breathing which involves the shoulders moving up with inhalation. I helped Lucy learn how to use abdominal breathing by focusing on her stomach muscles moving in and out and keeping her shoulders down and relaxed. Giving her simple instructions was more effective than a lengthy explanation of the mechanics of good breath support (as I sometimes do with patients). It was more important to learn the skill and get Lucy to the music. Basically, if her stomach moved out and her shoulders did not tense or move up then she was utilizing abdominal breathing techniques. We also worked on very soft singing and letting the air out slowly as she sang. (This breathing technique is similar to the "pursed lip" breathing technique used by respiratory therapists. Pursed lip breathing involves an inhalation followed by an exhalation through lips pursed with a small opening for air to come through.) This slow exhalation of air helps the body relax and allows for better singing of musical phrases. Once Lucy mastered this technique, we were able to delve more fully into the music. We sang many songs from Lucy's childhood with her spoken memories interspersed to give context to the songs. Lucy was able to reconnect with her music and memories *and* learn skills to help her breathe better.

Joseph seemed to love cigarettes more than life itself; at least it seemed like that to those of us who cared for him. His lungs were severely damaged by smoking and he was now in the final stages of his life. He had been on a list to receive a lung transplant; the only condition for him to receive the transplant was to stop smoking. In the end, Joseph was still unable to stop smoking. I worked with Joseph over the course of one year. We went through a lot of music during that time. One of his favorite songs was *I Sure Could Use a Little Goods News*, written by C. Black, R. Bourke and T. Rocco (1983): "One more sad story's one more than I can stand…we sure could use a little good news today." This song provided a lot of material for discussion during my early days of working with Joseph. Joseph also loved spirituals and, again during the early days, he readily sang them with me. Joseph frequently commented how much he appreciated live music. Clearly he felt there was something about the human

51

connection and the resonance of tone that could not be experienced with recorded music.

As with all lung diseases, breathing gradually became more difficult for Joseph. I worked with the music to help calm his fears and provide some reprieve from his illness. The songs and the music continued to bring him pleasure and comfort. As his health began to further decline, and he was less able to communicate verbally, I offered the familiar music he loved so well. His body responded to the music with slower and more even breathing. Music was able to accompany Joseph on his long journey with his disease, providing comfort and ease from his struggles into his final days.

I have used this song to emphasize the connection of the breath to the heart. Nina Wise has given me permission to reprint her lyrics here.

THE SWIM SONG
Nina Wise

Her mother taught her how to swim,
When she was very, very young
And swimming to survive, and swimming to survive.
The glide, she said, it's the most important part.
You kick, and then you glide,
You kick, and then you glide.

Keep breathing, it's the most important part.
It's all in the rhythm, it's all in the rhythm,
It's all in the rhythm of the heart.
It's all in the rhythm, it's all in the rhythm, it's all in the rhythm
Of the breathing, it's the most important part
You kick, and then you glide,
You kick and then you glide.

Keep breathing, it's the most important part.
It's all in the rhythm, it's all in the rhythm,
It's all in the rhythm of the heart.

MENTAL ILLNESS

Danielle had struggled with mental illness for most of her adult life, suffering primarily from anxiety, paranoia and hallucinations. Her situation was further complicated from severe arthritis and symptoms related to cancer. She had a hard time trusting people and would often strike out at those who were trying to help her. She used to sing, dance, and play the piano and ukulele but her medical condition severely limited her ability to participate in these activities. In the early days of our work together, she was able to sit at the piano in a wheelchair. Her fingers were stiff and bent from the arthritis but she was still able to bring them to the piano keys for the music. We played piano together or she would try to remember a melody and play it for me.

Danielle would sometimes complain at length with great agitation but her words did not follow a coherent train of thought. At these times, I was able to interrupt her with singing. She could easily stop talking and sing with me. It was like magic. Suddenly, we were engaged in meaningful activity and singing the same song; just moments before she was working herself into an agitated state. After the song, her mood was calm. We would then continue to sing together and use the breathing techniques

55

essential for singing to further help her feel calm. Eventually, her declining health confined her to her bed. Even with her poor health, I could usually still get her to sing with me. On one day, however, she was in a particularly ornery mood and refused to sing. When I turned to leave, she yelled at me with great irritation, "Hey, you're supposed to sing to me!"

Another person I worked with had a long-standing history of mental illness. **Eric** had been on anti-psychotic medication for most of his adult life. At this time, he was suffering from a severe case of *tardive dyskinesia*, a side effect of his anti-psychotic medication. Tardive dyskinesia is often visible as uncontrolled movements in the face, mouth and tongue. Eric's jaw was in constant and uncontrollable movement, averaging 180 movements per minute. I worked with Eric before his tardive dyskinesia had progressed to such a state, so I knew that he loved to sing. We discovered that, even with the tardive dyskinesia, when he sang his jaw relaxed and moved in a normal fashion with the music. In other words he did not experience the uncontrollable movements in his jaw. Our time singing together offered him a break from his symptoms. The singing also gave him an outlet to express his feelings via the lyrics of the songs he chose to sing.

The category of mental illness is extremely broad. It takes a skilled clinician to understand the complexities of the various mental health diagnoses and to provide a safe experience through music. In the right context, music can provide a container for safe exploration of feelings and self-expression.

Music therapist Lisa Jackert, MA, MT-BC, has spent much of her professional career working with people who have mental illness. The following is a chant she wrote and uses frequently in her groups with people dealing with a variety of mental health challenges.

WE HAVE COME THIS FAR
Lisa Jackert

I have come this far.

I have come this far.

Sometimes easy, sometimes hard.

I have come this far.

You have come this far.

You have come this far.

Sometimes easy, sometimes hard.

You have come this far.

We have come this far.

We have come this far.

Sometimes easy, sometimes hard.

We have come this far.

PHYSICAL CHALLENGES

Judy had been in a very serious automobile accident. She lost the use of her legs and needed a wheelchair for mobility. Her left arm had been amputated and she had a prosthesis that attached to her shoulder. She only had minimal use of her right arm and hand. She told me that she always wanted to play the guitar. I tuned a guitar to an open major chord and strapped it around her lap, laying it flat like a mountain dulcimer. The open chord in this case was a C major chord, meaning that all the strings were tuned to a C, E or G tone. Merely strumming the open strings was all that was needed to produce a pleasing sound. To add interest, I then made a capo that could attach to her prosthesis for her left hand. (A capo is a bar that is pressed across all the strings to change a chord or tuning.) She strummed with her right hand and chorded with the capo on her left hand prosthesis. I showed her how to play three different chords in the key of C. The chords were C major (open strum), F major (capo on the 5th fret) and G major (capo on the 7th fret). These three chords allowed her to play a variety of songs. We also worked on a familiar sounding chord progression called the *12 Bar Blues,* using the same three chords. This allowed us to add songwriting to our sessions in a blues style format. The blues were used for inspiration to write, discuss and sing about feelings of loss related to Judy's accident and current limitations.

Aaron had Cerebral Palsy and was unable to control many of the movements made by his body. He was unable to use his hands so he used a metal headband with a spoon attached to feed himself. He used his head to maneuver the spoon from his plate to his mouth. I replaced the spoon with a drumstick and set up three rototom drums next to him so he could manipulate his head to hit the drums with the drumstick. I consulted with a physical therapist to make certain that the head movements he used to drum were not harmful to him. He was delighted with his newfound musical skill. Aaron also played a shaker that was attached to a foot pedal. He used his foot to work the shaker and played the drum with his head. To further enhance the overall sound and experience, I added a cymbal to his other leg. One cymbal was attached to his knee, the other cymbal was attached to a stand just above that knee. He was able to pick his leg up to hit the cymbal. He would set the rhythm with the rototoms, add the shaker with one foot, and then add the cymbals for special effects. Aaron's delight with his music making was palpable, complete with big smiles and hearty laughs.

There are many ways in which instruments and music can be adapted to allow one to be more involved in music making and thus enhance quality of life. Physical limitations need not preclude making music. Adapting instruments to the physical needs of a client involves modifying parts of the instrument to fit; this can be challenging and fun. It's like trying to find the piece of the puzzle that will fit, or making your own piece to fit the puzzle. Instruments can be adapted, songs rearranged, and our expectations of sound can be amended to make room for all expressions of music.

The late Barry Bernstein and his daughter, Leah, wrote this song about acceptance and inclusion. Barry was a music therapist who touched many lives with his enthusiasm and caring heart. This song serves as a reminder that we are all "perfect just the way we are!"

BRIGHT LIGHT
Barry Bernstein & Leah Bernstein

I am a bright light
I am a bright light
I am a bright light
I am a bright light
I am a bright light
I am a bright light
Perfect just the way I am
Perfect just the way I am

Yellow, Brown, Black and White
Yellow, Brown, Black and White
Don't ya know we're all alright
Don't ya know we're all alright

Yellow, Brown, Black and White
Yellow, Brown, Black and White
Don't ya know we're all alright
Don't ya know we're all alright

YOUTH-AT-RISK

I worked with a musical theater project in Seattle that employed homeless youth in a production of *Man of La Mancha* (Leigh & Darion, 1986). Many of the youth were using drugs, engaging in prostitution, and often had to deal with violence on the streets. The project was an effort to help the youth transition out of this life on the streets. They received money for rehearsals and performances; they were also found permanent housing and given food. Throughout this theater project, we worked with the youth on issues and themes from the play that resonated with the very real drama in their lives, and, of course, the notion of dreaming "the impossible dream."

At their young ages, their lives were already filled with incredible physical and emotional struggles. Low self-esteem was evidenced with drooped head and shoulders, arms hanging low, and self-deprecating comments made during casual conversations. My official role was to help the youth with vocal technique for the production. The music of *Man of La Mancha* was not easy to sing but the youth rose to the challenge. I found that our work with singing technique helped to address their low self-esteem. Good vocal technique requires the body to be upright and the head held high; this maximizes breath support and enhances tonal production and quality. A head held high had the additional benefit of communicating, "I am somebody" and "Listen to me, I have something to say (sing)." It helped that the improved posture allowed them make a more beautiful vocal sound. The better they sounded the more proud they were of themselves. It was exciting to work with them, see their progress, and hear their beautiful voices singing out with heads held high!

I wrote this song in reflection of the many needs of our children that go unmet. When I was in graduate school for social work more than 20 years ago, an estimated 20% of the poor in our nation were children. That figure remains virtually the same to this day (National Poverty Center, 2011, ¶13).

HUSH-A-BYE

Barbara Dunn / opening verse traditional

Hush-a-bye, don't cry, go to sleep little one.
When you wake, you shall have all the pretty little horses.

Hush a-bye, don't cry
Go to sleep little one.
When you wake, you shall have
Food and shelter and a home.

In this wealthy nation
Children should have a home.
In this wealthy nation,
Children should have food.
There's so much talk of family values
But there's no value if it's hunger and it's you.

A little child sleeps tonight
Under a cold, dark bridge.
The little child weeps tonight
Shivering in the cold.
Her mother holds her close to warm her
As she cries out hoping to be heard.

ABOUT MUSIC THERAPY

The following section explores the development of music therapy as a profession. With roots in the early 20th century, many people have contributed to the field along the way. I wrote the following chant in dedication to music therapist Dr. Tony Wigram for the 2010 annual conference for the American Music Therapy Association. Dr. Wigram was a gifted music therapist, researcher and professor who contributed volumes to the music therapy profession. Sadly, he passed away from cancer in June, 2011. More than 900 attendees at the conference sang this for Tony during the opening session.

Let love surround you
And keep you safe and warm.
May the music in our hearts
Be a shelter from the storm.

Introduction to Music Therapy in the United States

While music has likely been used for healing since humans first evolved, the more organized profession of music therapy in the United States has roots in the early 20th century. *An Introduction to Music Therapy: Theory and Practice* (Davis, Gfeller, & Thaut, 1992) provides a comprehensive exploration of this history. This textbook highlights some interesting information about early contributions to the field. Eva Vescelius promoted the use of music as therapy in her 1913 publication entitled *Music and Health.* Margaret Anderton and Isa Maud Ilsen taught classes on "musicotherapy" at New York City's Columbia University in 1919. These classes prepared musicians to work in hospitals as therapists. Ilsen also formed the National Association for Music in Hospitals in 1926. During the 1930s, Harriet Ayer Seymour was involved with a Federal Music Project of the Works Progress Administration (WPA) under the Roosevelt Administration. This project involved the use of music at hospitals and prisons in New York City (pp. 26-30). The profession of music therapy gained momentum after World War II with music assisting veterans suffering from "shell shock," a condition that today is called Post Traumatic Stress Disorder (PTSD). The 1940s also saw the first degree program and core classes to be offered in music therapy at Michigan State

69

University and Kansas University. Robert Unkefer and E. Thayer Gaston were pioneers during these early stages of professional music therapy. In 1968, Gaston edited the book *Music in Therapy*. For many years, this book was the primary text for training programs in music therapy. In 1950, the National Association for Music Therapy (NAMT) was established. Until 1998 there were two national music therapy associations: NAMT and the American Association for Music Therapy (AAMT), established in 1971. The two associations merged in 1998 to form the American Music Therapy Association (AMTA). AMTA publishes a quarterly newsletter, the quarterly research Journal of Music Therapy, and a semi-annual clinical publication entitled Perspectives. The Journal of Music Therapy has been in existence since 1964. That is nearly half a century of quantifiable data on the efficacy of using music as therapy!

Typically, music therapy sessions are designed with goals and objectives that address a nonmusical area and are specific to the client or group. For example, a goal for someone recovering from a stroke might be to relearn how to talk. Specific objectives might include singing to achieve a speech related goal. Music therapists often work collaboratively with other disciplines, such as nursing, social work, occupational, physical and speech therapy. This type of collaboration can greatly enhance the therapeutic process.

The 2010 AMTA Member Sourcebook estimated that in 2009, 1.2 million people received music therapy services in 30,600 facilities. Additionally, twice as many new music therapy jobs were created than were lost during 2009 (p. 206). For more information about the field, visit the American Music Therapy Association at http://www.musictherapy.org.

Training for Music Therapy

To become a music therapist in the United States, students must complete a bachelor or master's degree in music therapy at an accredited program. Students must also complete 1200 hours of clinical training. After completing the degree, she or he is then eligible to sit for the Music Therapy Board Certification exam. Upon passing the exam, the student is granted the title MT-BC (Music Therapist-Board Certified). Continuing education credits are required to maintain this certification.

The music therapy degree program includes an extensive array of music classes along with courses in music therapy, psychology, physiology, social and behavioral sciences, disabilities, and general studies. The thorough study of music equips the music therapist with skills that include composition, conducting, musical performance (both solo and ensemble), and an advanced knowledge of music theory. I have found this extensive musical training to be invaluable in my work. It allows me to focus on the therapeutic process rather than concentrating on musical technique. Knowledge of other instruments has also been very helpful. I once worked with a woman who was 100 and hadn't played the violin in 80 years. Even though I am not a violinist, I knew enough about the violin to tune it, rosin the bow and then put it into her hands. She was thrilled to once again hold the bow and feel the vibrations of her music as she played the strings.

In an effort to create more opportunities for singing, four of my music therapy colleagues and I formed the Daughters of Harriet, named after Harriet Ayer Seymour – one of the founding mothers of music therapy. We have been leading large chant circles at conferences and in our individual communities. We begin leading a song/chant with a seed song that is generally short and easy to learn; the songs grow as they are sung – harmonies and rounds are added, and dancing has erupted on more than one occasion. The following is one I wrote in honor of Harriet Seymour.

HARRIET SEYMOUR
Barbara Dunn

We are the Daughters of Harriet.

Her song flows through us and to you.

If you listen closely,

You can feel it, too.

Living this moment

And loving the beauty.

SELECTED RESEARCH

Numerous studies have been conducted on the therapeutic uses of music. They have been conducted through the lens of a variety of professions, such as music therapy, gerontology, cardiology and oncology. All of the studies continue to add to our knowledge base of how music can help people. The following selected studies highlight the variety of research that has been conducted in this area.

Music Assisted Relaxation Decreases Anxiety

In a study by S.L. Robb, R.J. Nichols, R.L. Rutan, B.L. Bishop, and J.C. Parker, (1995), it was found that Music Assisted Relaxation (MAR) was significantly more effective in decreasing anxiety than standard preoperative interventions for surgical patients. The MAR "included music listening, deep diaphragmatic breathing, progressive muscle relaxation, and imagery" (p. 2). The criteria for the selected music included "a tempo at or below a resting heart rate (72 bpm or less), predictable dynamics, fluid melodic movement (predominantly by step), pleasing harmonies, regular rhythm without sudden changes, and tonal qualities that include strings, flute, and/or piano" (p. 7).

The subjects for the study were pediatric burn patients who ranged from 8 – 20 years in age. The experimental group was given the MAR intervention several times: the evening before surgery, in the patient's room the morning of surgery, during transport to surgery, in the surgical suite, and postoperatively in the recovery room. The control group only received standard preoperative interventions that included a session with the child life specialist who used pictures and props to help explain the surgical process to the patient. The control group did not receive MAR. Anxiety levels for both groups were measured with State-

Trait Anxiety Index for Children before interventions and surgery and again after surgery. The experimental group also was interviewed and completed a questionnaire after their surgeries. Results of the study indicated a significant reduction in anxiety for patients who received MAR. The level of anxiety for these patients was considerably lower than for those who did not receive MAR. Additionally, patients that received MAR stated they would use it again for future surgeries.

Music and Stories Help Children with Autism

In a creative approach to helping children with autism, researcher M.D. Brownell (2002) found that music combined with an original story can enhance learning of specific social skills. Brownell based his research on "social stories" developed by Carol Gray in 1993. Social stories are original stories that address target behaviors that adversely affect the life of a student and those around him or her.

In Brownell's study, he worked with four boys who had autism as a primary diagnosis. Each of the children had a target behavior identified by their respective teachers. A story was then written for each child that addressed his targeted behavior. The stories were placed in a book with one to two sentences on each page and an appropriate illustration. Music was composed using the sentences for lyrics. Data was collected that recorded the number of times the target behavior occurred, either without the social story (baseline) or immediately following the story that was either read or sung.

One of the young boy's target behaviors was his use of a very loud shouting voice that was disturbing to his classmates and the milieu of the classroom. Here is the story written for him:

Using a Quiet Voice

Sometimes I need to use a quiet voice. People might talk loudly when they are outside. People talk quietly when they are inside. If I talk quietly inside, my friends and teachers can still hear me. If I yell inside, I might scare my friends and teachers. I don't like to scare anyone. I will try to talk quietly inside. (p.128)

Results of the study found that target behaviors decreased after the social story was either read or sung to the child. The target behaviors occurred with the least frequency just after the musical story.

Music Therapy Boosts the Immune System for People with Cancer

It is well known that cancer and the treatment of cancer can compromise the immune system. In her landmark study, D. Lane (1994) found that a single 30-minute music therapy session could significantly increase the immune response, Immunoglobulin A, in hospitalized children. Immunoglobulin A (IgA) is an immune system response that is secreted by mucosal cells and is one of the first lines of defense against upper respiratory infections. Low levels of IgA are considered to correlate with greater frequencies of illness.

Lane worked with 38 children at a major university hospital in Ohio. Patients in the experimental group received 30 minutes of music therapy that included singing; identifying, passing, and playing musical instruments; and imitation and listening activities. Patients assigned to the control group did not receive music therapy but continued with whatever activity they were involved in at the time, i.e., reading, drawing, video games. The children's salivary IgA levels were obtained before the 30-minute session and at the end of the session. Significant increases in IgA levels were found after the 30-minute music therapy session as compared with the control group.

Pacifier-Activated-Lullaby (PAL) Nourishes Preemies

J.M. Standley (2003) researched the use of music to increase the feeding rate for premature babies. She developed a pacifier that elicited lullabies when the baby sucked on it. These infants were typically not sucking for nourishment. Standley found that once the preemies learned to suck with the musical reinforcement, this skill could be transferred to nutritional feeding, which, in turn, significantly increased the feeding rates for preemies.

Standley has continued her research on this topic and has designed the Pacifier-Activated-Lullaby (PAL) to help premature babies learn the necessary skill of sucking. The PAL is available from Powers Device Technologies, Inc. (www.powersdt.com). According to their website, Standley's research found that preemies "increased their sucking rates 2.5 times when exposed to music, thus helping to increase their weight.... Standley's musical pacifier has demonstrated what have been called "amazing" results in repeated tests done at Tallahassee Memorial Hospital" (Powers Device Technologies , n.d., ¶ 3).

Music Therapy Enhances Quality of Life for Hospice Patients

R.E. Hilliard (2003) found that music therapy increased the quality of life for patients who received hospice care. This was true even as patient's health declined. The study assessed 80 hospice patients using the Hospice Quality of Life Index-Revised (HQLI-R) and the Palliative Performance Scale (PPS) as measurement tools. Patients were randomly assigned to two groups: the control group received routine hospice services (nursing care, home health aid, spiritual care, counselor, and volunteers, as requested); the experimental group received routine hospice services plus music therapy services.

All subjects had terminal cancer with six months or less to live and were newly admitted hospice patients. They all lived in their own homes, there were equal numbers of men and women, and the average age was 65 years old.

The self-reporting questionnaire HQLI-R was administered after each music therapy (experimental group) or counseling session (control group). It asked questions related to daily activity, social life, ability to concentrate, enjoyable activity, anger, nausea, pain, sex life, worry, anxiety, spirituality (includes meaning in life), physical contact, family support, and relationship with God. Higher scores on the HQLI-R were associated with a higher perceived quality of life.

The PPS measured physical status in palliative care and was administered routinely during nursing visits. Areas assessed by the PPS included conscious level, intake, self-care, ambulation, activity, and evidence of disease.

Music therapy sessions were designed to meet individual needs of the patients. Music therapists used live music that was selected by the clients. The music included singing, music listening, lyric analysis, instrument playing, song parody, and song gifts. Music therapists were more likely to address nausea and vomiting, pain, comfort measures, confusion, semi-coma, and changes in locus of control than were the counselors in the control group.

The results of the HQLI-R scores for quality of life were significantly higher for the experimental group after the initial music therapy visit and continued to increase with subsequent visits. Quality of life was increased with music therapy even while physical health declined. For the control group, quality of life scores decreased after the second counselor's visit.

According to Hilliard,

"These data are important because they illustrate that music therapy treatment served to increase quality of life initially

84

and increase quality of life even more over time. These data support the use of music therapy treatment for patients upon admission into hospice and its provision with high frequency throughout their remaining lifetime." (p. 131)

Music Helps Patients with Lung Disease Go the Distance

G. Bauldoff, L. Hoffman, T. Zullo, and F. Sciurba (2002) found that listening to music while walking proved to be beneficial to patients with moderate to severe COPD. They conducted an eight-week study with twenty-four patients following completion of a pulmonary rehabilitation program. All subjects were instructed to walk at their own pace for 20-45 minutes, two to five times per week. The experimental group (12 subjects) listened to music on portable audiocassette players while they walked. The music consisted of two audiocassettes with country/western, classical, pop/Motown and big band music. The control group did not use music on their walk.

The distance walked in a six-minute period was measured at the beginning, middle and end of the study. Results found that the experimental group was able to *increase* their distance by an average of 445 feet, while the control group's distance actually decreased an average of 169 feet. Results also demonstrated that subjects who used music on their walk perceived significantly less dyspnea (shortness of breath) than those who did not use music.

TOOLS OF THE TRADE

I use a variety of tools in my work, such as songwriting, music-assisted relaxation, and/or singing. The specific tools I use change with the needs of any given moment. For example, with the same patient I might use songwriting to help communicate feelings one week and the next week engage her or him in relaxation to live music. I like to think of all of my tools and related skills as fitting into a large bag (figuratively and, sometimes, literally). I carry this bag with me always. In addition to the above-mentioned examples, this bag includes songs my mother sang to me when I was young, songs I learned in school, from friends, on the streets, or from clients. In this bag there may be a guitar, a keyboard, a dulcimer, a couple of recorders, some rhythm instruments or whatever else might be needed for the session. Some days the bag is quite large. Other days I just bring my guitar and a bag filled with songs. When a session begins I am never quite sure what will be needed from the bag, but I am ready. I have been known to pull out an Italian aria in the middle of a hospital hallway. The following sections highlight some of the tools I have found to be most useful.

Relaxation with Music and Entrainment

Some of the more frequent referrals I receive are to help people with anxiety. I often use Progressive Muscle Relaxation (PMR) with music specifically chosen by my client that assists her or him in feeling relaxed. PMR is a technique that instructs a person to relax (or tense and then relax) parts of the body in a systematic manner. For example, begin with the head, focus attention on the forehead, jaw, etc., and relax them (or tense and relax them), next the focus is on the shoulders and down through to the feet.

After we have worked with the breath and relaxing the muscles, I bring in the music and instruct my client to let the music come in through their head and move through their body in the same way their breath is moving through. I might then have her or him bring an image or place to mind that they have identified as relaxing. I instruct him or her to allow their mind and body to fully embrace and enjoy this image or place. I elaborate or simplify this process depending on my client's needs and ability to work with the process.

Frequently I use a technique called entrainment. This involves matching the rhythm of the music to the rhythm of the client. This can be an especially useful tool when a client is not conscious or otherwise cognitively present. Their breathing and body movements reflect an internal rhythm. I match that rhythm with my music. Once we are locked into the same rhythm, I am able to gradually adjust the rhythm to a slower, more relaxed pace.

Improvisation

Improvisation provides an opportunity for someone to jump right into playing music, even if they have never played before. The best way I have found to do this is to set it up so there are few notes to choose from and all the notes sound good together. A pentatonic scale can be very useful for this purpose – all the notes in this 5-note scale sound good together. Additionally, there may or may not be a designated tonal center. This offers more opportunity for creating melodies because the ear is not drawn to match a previously heard tune. Instruments that are good for improvisation are ones that you can manipulate or predetermine the notes that are available to play, such as a xylophone or playing only the black keys on the piano.

Other musical scales I have found useful for improvising are modes. Modal scales are 8-tone scales or scales that are made up of notes with various arrangements of half and whole steps. The most familiar mode to our Western ear is the Ionian, also called the major scale. Early music utilized a variety of modal tonalities. The simplest way to envision the common eight modes is with the white keys on the piano. Begin on one white key and end on the same white key an octave higher and the scale will represent one of the modes. The following are the names of the modes in ascending order, beginning with C on the white keys of the piano:

Ionian, Dorian, Phrygian, Lydian, Mixolydian, Aolean and Locrian.

Forrest Kinney (2004) has created *Pattern Play*: a method of improvisation for the piano that makes the entire process very accessible. Pattern Play primarily involves a repeating pattern played by the left hand with free improvisation in the right hand. Kinney has many patterns to choose from with each one creating a very different feel and sound. I am always amazed at the simplicity of this method with the resulting sound being beautifully musical. I have used this method of piano playing frequently with clients in music therapy. It provides an avenue to tap into the heart of the music and gets them playing, even if they have not played before. For someone who is ill and always wanted to play the piano, this method allows them to do just that in a matter of minutes.

Musical Conversations

Playing instrumental music can bypass the need to find the right "words" to explain how we feel. Sometimes a greater depth of feelings can be communicated via the emotional tone of the music than through lyrics in a song. I often use instrumental music to have a two-way conversation with someone that is not encumbered with words. We might do this through melodic instruments, such as guitar, piano, or flute. Drums can also provide an expressive route to communication. The idea is to mimic a verbal conversation using music instead of spoken words. Common knowledge tells us that communication occurs on many levels with the actual words being only one element of the conversation. Body language and tonal inflection contribute substantially to an exchange.

I often utilize kazoos with children who are unable to use words to communicate. Kazoos offer communication tools of inflection and body language and they have the added benefit of being fun. They encourage an element of silliness that can be disarming and level the playing field of communication. I have experienced true reciprocal interactions with people who are barely able to give eye contact or verbal responses to anyone.

Several years ago I found myself working with a woman who was in her 90s and electively mute. She could talk but, for

93

whatever reason, chose not to. During her lifetime, she had raised children, worked as a doctor and a researcher; she also used to play the piano and loved music. With great effort, I could sometimes entice her to play the piano. I was unable to get her to sing until one day, on a whim, I gave her a kazoo. She put the kazoo to her mouth and began to sing! Her daughter happened to be present that day and was brought to tears when she heard her mother's voice. She had not heard her mother's voice in more than two years. In subsequent sessions, it was always the kazoo that brought out her voice.

Power Songs

This is my own term for the intentional use of songs that are sung aloud or silently in your head to create a desired feeling or experience. These identified songs might elicit a feeling of well-being, peace, comfort, or energy. They can be called upon at any time to help get through a difficult time.

I first experimented with this myself while competing in a triathlon. I was at the front of the pack for the swim leg of the race. I figured that if I had a great song in my head, with a good steady beat, I could keep motivated for the swim. I chose an old Motown song called *Ball of Confusion*. Somehow, the title of the song fit the scene of so many bodies lined up to plow through the waters at 8 a.m. on that Saturday morning. With the song and the espresso I had on my way to the event, I was propelled through the water. About ten minutes into the swim my body and mind started to falter. (The week before the triathlon I had been at a guitar camp where I averaged two to five hours of sleep per night.) So there I was, already into the swim, and I began to panic because I was not sure my body could make it. The event sponsors had support people on boats in the water to help the swimmers. I spoke with one of them when I first began to panic. His response was to tell me how he hates to swim. (Where did they get this guy?) I knew I had to figure it out for myself. I worked with people who had panic attacks. Now what was it I told them to do? I slowed my swim stroke down and used my breath to help myself relax. I knew I had to change the song in my head; I just could not keep up with Motown. I had learned a beautiful song at camp the previous week that a fellow camper, Luther Schutz (1997), wrote: "I can hear it. I am near it. I've been searching for some time. It has found you. It surrounds you. A cathedral in your mind. Voices resonate the past. And harmonies are like stained glass. Did I really see? Somebody smiled at me." I could only remember the first verse of the song but that would have to do. I used the song and my breath to continue with the swim. Although it seemed like I was swimming for several hours, I was actually out of the water within thirty minutes time. Luther's song helped to pull me through!

I work with my clients to identify songs that will give them strength, courage, or whatever else they need. We sing the songs, they close their eyes and hear the songs in their heads; they find a comfort that is accessible to them even when their bodies are failing them. These songs are available when they are in need of comfort or strength, such as on an operating table or dealing with a difficult situation. The songs can be brought to mind and work in the same way that breathing and bringing a pleasing place or experience to mind can decrease stress or anxiety.

Songwriting

In therapy, expression of feelings is often at the heart of the work with an individual or group. For this reason, writing songs can be a very useful and powerful tool. Song lyrics can give thoughts and feelings an expressive vehicle and put them into a package that can then be viewed from different angles. This can be helpful when trying to get a new perspective on a troubling issue. The music can further help to express the related emotions. They might address feelings of isolation, depression, anger, fear, or joy. They might also be used to assist someone, especially a child, in understanding concepts from appropriate boundaries to academic skills.

There are a variety of techniques I use for songwriting in therapy, from improvisation to re-writing words to familiar tunes to writing the entire song from scratch. I have created songs on the spot that incorporated information and stories about a client's life and sung them to the client. This was particularly useful when a client was unable to speak or communicate, as with someone who has mental confusion or dementia. I worked with a man in a nursing home who was no longer able to speak or otherwise communicate. I used to sing stories of his life to him with information gathered from family members and chart notes.

There would be occasional moments when he would look directly at me with a big smile.

Songwriting is also my personal process for making sense of my work and life and of this world. In some ways, I write because I have to. It is a way to get thoughts out of my head; adding the music and poetry lends beauty and color to the process. To me, adding music to words is like turning off the fluorescent lights and eating dinner by candlelight. Songwriting offers a way to give voice to the essence of who we are and allows us to understand and express ourselves and, to some extent, our relationship to the community and world that surrounds us.

Singing

One of my lifetime missions has been to help others find the same comfort in their singing voice that I have enjoyed. Regardless of whether I am in *good voice*, my voice is available to me and can provide comfort at a moment's notice. To me, singing is a natural expression, like breathing. I find it sad that some people do not sing even though they say they would like to. In my years as a music therapist and voice teacher, I have heard a wide variety of reasons why people do not sing: "My third grade music teacher asked me to mouth the words in choir," or "I couldn't carry a tune in a bucket." I grew up in a household where singing was just something we did. My mother sang opera as she cleaned the house. My siblings and I were known for our lively version of *Bohemian Rhapsody*, sung while dish washing. In some parts of the world, entire communities sing and sing well! When I lived in New Zealand (Aoteatoa), I often heard people talk of the glorious voices of the Maori people. Singing is a culturally supported activity in Maori communities. Naturally their voices sound wonderful – they have been singing their entire lives. There are countries in Africa where children can sing up to 100 songs by the time they are five. They don't question or analyze their singing ability. They just sing. Yet, in other countries, like the United States, many seem to believe that either people are born with musical abilities or they are not.

With the exception of hearing impairment or physical problems with the voice, I do not believe there is a physiological explanation for the inability to sing. Like they say in Zimbabwe, "If you can talk, you can sing!" It takes some concentration to hear the pitches in your head and then to match those pitches with your voice. When we hear songs in our heads, they are in tune. It is in the passage from the head to the mouth that difficulties occur. If the head is filled with negative messages regarding the ability or inability to sing then it will be even harder to sing.

For several years I taught private voice lessons, directed a women's vocal ensemble, and led a church choir. I worked with singers who had a wide range of experiences and varying degrees of confidence with their abilities. Some singers did have difficulties staying in tune. I would practice with them using the following technique: I sang one line to a song, had them repeat the line in their head, and then they sang it back to me, all in the exact time of the music. Every time we used that technique, they were able to sing the line in tune!

I have also worked with individuals who desperately wanted to get past "something" that prevented them from singing. They often had negative messages in their heads about their voice. Tied

100

to these messages might have been memories of ridicule or even abuse. I have worked with people who were so traumatized that their voice would actually close up when they tried to sing. They were unable to make a sound. Helping them to produce a vocal sound was sometimes just the catalyst needed to begin healing deep-seated wounds.

There are many ways to bring singing more fully into our lives. The first step is to just sing. Singing improves with singing. Even the most glorious voice will sound rusty if it is not used. The more we sing, the more comfortable we are with singing. The more we sing, the better our vocal muscles will be toned. The more we sing…

MUSIC AND SELF-CARE

Playing music is one of the best things I can do to reduce my own personal stress. When I sit down at the piano and begin to play and sing, my entire body breathes a sigh of relief. A spirit from deep inside moves through me; I am at ease with the music and myself. I know that when I am not singing regularly, stress builds and everyone around me suffers; just ask my family. Singing is essential to my relief of stress and my overall health. In addition, the rhythm and flow of my daily life is off-balance when music making is not incorporated.

Most people acknowledge that playing music is fun and can be a great tool for self-care. Yet, an often-heard complaint is: "I just don't have *time* to play music." Even the word "time" can bring up strong feelings and a sigh of defeat for many people. "If only I had more time..." "One more phone call and then I'll have time to play music." Well, maybe it is not really about time. Perhaps it has more to do with taking care of ourselves and placing value on that care. Self-care is about prioritizing our health and well-being. Another part of self-care has to do with self-worth. Maybe it is difficult to prioritize music making because we do not feel deserving of such indulgence. It seems an unwritten value in our culture that it is okay to do something as long as it benefits others. It is okay to provide music for other people, but when the recipient of the music is the musician herself, it somehow feels different. It is fine to play music at the end of the day – *after* all other work is done. Playing music during the busy workday is a different matter. Yet, one three-minute song can change a mood in the time it takes to sing it. It might be just enough to decrease the singer's blood pressure or help to refocus on a challenging work project.

A lasting memory of my music therapy internship more than twenty-five years ago, was the band that was comprised of our entire music therapy department: eight musicians in total. We all worked at a large psychiatric hospital in Texas. Every Friday we played music for a dance on one of the units at the hospital. Sometimes the patients got up and sang with us; sometimes they just danced. We had a blast playing old rock-and-roll and country western songs. It was fun for the patients and a great way for us to end our work-week.

CLOSING COMMENTS

Music therapy has offered me the creative freedom to use music in many different ways, from transcending pain to venting anger. I feel honored by the trust given to me by my patients and their families in our work together with music, along with all the related emotions that accompanied their struggles. In the Buddhist practice of loving-kindness, thoughts of love and kindness that are sent out to others, in turn, come back to the sender. This same concept applies to music therapy: when you put out music with the intent to help others, you receive the music. I, too, can be calmed by the music (or energized), which further helps to facilitate the therapeutic process. I have been awed by the power of music to create sacred space around a dying person with the shared voices of their loved ones. I have been equally thrilled to experience the sheer delight as an otherwise reserved child enthusiastically joined the group in making music. I have felt satisfaction in witnessing someone finally expressing his or her long-buried emotions through music. These situations in music therapy have been palpable, and I have been so moved. Empathic connections such as these are the cornerstone of this work. It is the heartfelt connections with people that promote change, growth and healing.

105

There are so many ways to contribute to our world. In the words of Jana Stanfield (2003), "I cannot do all the good that the world needs. But the world needs all the good that I can do." For me, using music to help people has been compelling and rewarding work; it has felt like "the good I can do." The words in this book are simply a part of my journey. They are not the complete story, they are moments in time – moments transformed by music.

AT THE END OF THE DAY
Barbara Dunn

At the end of the day, I can honestly say,
I gave what I had to give,
Brought peace where the light was dim.
It was all I could do; give the best that I knew.
And that was enough.

Through a patchwork of caring I pieced it together,
Choosing colors that favored each other.
The seams they were strong and love is not wrong.
What's left can keep me warm.

At the end of the day, I can honestly say,
I gave what I had to give,
Brought peace where the light was dim.
It was all I could do; give the best that I knew.
And that was enough.

With the cruelties in life, I'd take up your fight,
So your burdens could be a bit lighter.
Yea, the seas they'd get rough and I'm not all that tough
But your light brightened my way.

We never really know our path.
We can see where we've been not where we'll go.
So I'll stay with the mystery,
Behold what I feel and what I see.

At the end of the day, I can honestly say,
I gave what I had to give,
Brought peace where the light was dim.
It was all I could do; give the best that I knew.
And that was enough.

REFERENCES

American Music Therapy Association. (2010). *AMTA member sourcebook 2010*. Silver Spring, MD: Author.

American Music Therapy Association (AMTA). Silver Spring, MD. http://www.musictherapy.org

Author Unknown, "It's a long goodbye", Reprinted from *Midlife orphan* by Jane Brooks (p.47-48). NY: Berkley Book.

Bauldoff, G., Hoffman, L., Zullo, T., & Sciurba, F. (2002). Exercise maintenance following pulmonary rehabilitation: Effect of distractive stimuli. *American College of Chest Physicians (CHEST), 122,* 948-954.

Bernstein, B. & Bernstein, L. (1996). Bright light. On *Barry Bernstein, Songs of the spirit*. Healthy Sounds Publishing.

Black, C., Bourke, R., & Rocco, T. (1983). A little good news [A. Murray]. On *A little good news*. Capital Records.

Brownell, M. D. (2002). Musically adapted social stories to modify behaviors in students with autism: Four case studies. *Journal of Music Therapy, 39*(2), 117-144.

Cohen, L. (1971). Joan of arc [J. Warnes]. On *Famous blue raincoat, Songs of Leonard Cohen*. Private Music. (1986)

Davis, W., Gfeller, K., & Taut, M. (1992). *An introduction to music therapy: Theory and practice*. Dubuque, IA: Wm. C. Brown Publishers.

Gaston, E.T. (Ed.). (1968). *Music in therapy*. New York: Macmillan Co.

Gordon & Warren. (1941). Chattanooga choo choo [Glenn Miller Orchestra]. Twentieth Century Music Corporation.

Hill, B. (1936). The glory of love [B. Midler]. On *Beaches original soundtrack recording*. Atlantic Records. (1990)

Hilliard, R.E. (2003). The effects of music therapy on the quality and length of life of people diagnosed with terminal cancer. *Journal of Music Therapy, (40)*2, 113–137.

Huxley, A. (1931). *Music at night and other essays.* Garden City, NY: Country Life Press, Doubleday Doran & Company, Inc.

Jackert, L. (2010). We have come this far. Email for Lisa Jackert: ljmt4u@yahoo.com

Kern, J. & Hammerstein, O. (1927). Ol man river [P. Robeson]. From Broadway musical *Show Boat.*

Kinney, F. (2004). *Pattern play: Volume 1-A.* Two Streams Press.

Lane, D. (1994). Effects of music therapy on immune function of hospitalized patients. *Quality of Life Research, (3)*4, 74-80.

Leigh, M. & Darion, J. (1986). *Man of LaMancha.* Cherry Lane Music.

McCutcheon, J. (1984). Christmas in the trenches. On *Winter solstice.* Rounder Records. (1992)

National Poverty Center. (2011). How many children live in poverty? Retrieved from *Poverty in the United States* National Poverty Center at University of Michigan, http://www.npc.umich.edu/poverty/#5.

Powers Device Technologies (n.d.). Research by Dr. Jayne Standley. *Powers Direct Technologies.* Retrieved December 19, 2011 from http://powersdt.com/research-by-dr-jayne-standley/

Robb, S.L., Nichols, R.J., Rutan, R.L., Bishop, B.L. & Parker, J. C. (1995). The effects of music assisted relaxation on preoperative anxiety. *Journal of Music Therapy, (32)*1, 2-21.

Seeger, P. (1969). Old devil time. On *Singalong Sanders theater, 1980.* Smithsonian Folkways Recording. (1992)

Schutz, L. (1997). Somebody smiled [Equinox]. On *Wake up in the moonlight singing.*

Standley, J.M. (2003). The effect of music-reinforced non-nutritive sucking on feeding rate of premature infants. *Journal of Pediatric Nursing, 18*(3), 169-173.

Stanfield, J. (2003). All the good. On *Let the change begin.* Relatively Famous Records.

Stevens, C. (1971). Moonshadow. On *Teaser and the firecat.* EMI Music Publishing.

Wise, N. (1984). The swim song. For more information about Nina Wise and her music, go to http://www.ninawise.com

BOOKS and RECORDINGS
by Barbara Dunn

Books

- Music and Solidarity, Felicity Laurence and Olivier Urbain, editors (2011). *Peace & Policy,* volume 15. Transaction Publishers.

  Chapter: "Music Therapy: Connecting through Music"
- Transforming Conflict Through Music (2008), available through ProQuest.

Recordings

- You Are A Song (2010), recorded with Daughters of Harriet, original songs and chants
- The Sparrow Takes Flight (1998), solo album of original and traditional songs

About the Author

Barbara Dunn, PhD, LICSW, MT-BC has been working in the field of music therapy for more than 25 years. She was born in Detroit, Michigan, studied music therapy at Michigan State University, and completed her graduate studies in social work at the University of Washington. She followed this work with post-graduate studies in ethnomusicology at Victoria University in New Zealand with an emphasis on how people in various cultures around the world used music to address social work concerns. She completed her doctoral work at Union Institute and University in Conflict Transformation and Music. Her research focused on bringing music into the process of mediation.

Barbara is a licensed clinical social worker with a private psychotherapy/music therapy practice in Seattle, WA. She also directs the music therapy program at Whidbey General Hospital in Coupeville, WA. She is available for keynote presentations, workshops, and musical performances.

www.barbaradunn.com